Little Sticker Dolly Dressing Rainbow fairy

Written by Fiona Watt
Illustrated by Lizzie Mackay
Designed by Antonia Miller
and Johanna Furst

Contents

Ruby the rainbow fairy

Ruby lives in a magical castle high up in the sky.
On rainy days, when the sun peeks through the clouds,
she loves to make rainbows.

Dress Ruby in her fairy clothes, then decorate
the pages with the rest of the stickers.

Above Fairyland

The sky is beginning to fill with rain clouds as Ruby flies over Fairyland. She's off to gather fairy dust to make her rainbows. Far below her, fairies are fluttering around the trees.

Poppy

Red petals

Poppy's garden is filled with flowers, shiny berries and little bugs. The bugs help Ruby and Poppy collect red fairy dust.

Ruby

Marigold

Yellow meadow

Bees hover and butterflies dance around the yellow buttercups, dandelions and sunflowers that grow in the meadow.

Briar

Green leaves

Beneath the trees, Briar and Ruby are searching for lucky four-leaf clovers. Have they found what they are looking for?

Ruby

Blue berries

Ruby is picking berries from the bushes that grow beside a clear blue stream. Dragonflies dart around and fish swim in the water.

Ruby

Sapphire

Violet
Indigo

Ruby

Indigo and Violet

Ruby's friends Indigo and Violet are helping her gather fairy dust. Dark blue birds and little purple creatures help, too.

Rainbow flowers

As Ruby waves her wand, a rainbow of fairy dust flies through the air, turning flowers into red, orange, yellow, green, blue, indigo and violet.

Ruby

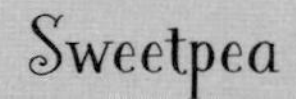

Magical butterflies

Ruby wafts her wand from side to side.
As butterflies flutter around, the fairy dust
changes their wings to rainbows.

Ruby

Painting the sky

With a final sweep of her wand, Ruby paints a massive rainbow across the sky. The shades appear in fluffy clouds and raindrops, too.

Fading away

As the sun sets at the end of the day,
the sky darkens and Ruby's rainbow
gradually fades away.

This edition first published in 2020 by Usborne Publishing Ltd., Usborne House, 83-85 Saffron Hill, London, EC1N 8RT, England. usborne.com

UE This edition first published in America 2020.

Ruby the rainbow fairy

Pages 2–3

Castle roofs

Roofs for the castle

Above Fairyland

Pages 4–5

Put Ruby's top on after her skirt

Flowers for Ruby's hair

More stickers for Above Fairyland
Pages 4–5
Red petals
Pages 6–7
Put the fairies' skirts on before their tops.
Poppy's top
Flowers for Ruby's hair
Poppy's skirt
Ruby's outfit
A bug for Ruby to hold

Orange grove

Pages 8–9

Yellow meadow

Pages 10–11